77 ROUNDS AND CANONS

compiled and edited by

KENNETH SIMPSON

NOVELLO PUBLISHING LIMITED
14 –15 Berners Street, London W1T 3LJ, UK

Order No. NOV192021

CONTENTS

FOREWORD

I hope that this collection of rounds and canons will give as much pleasure as my two previous sets, *A First Round Book*, and *Rounds for Christmas* (both Novello) seem to have done. As in the earlier books, most of the items are musically straightforward and of moderate compass, but I have also included such splendid music as the Mozart *Ave Maria* (No. 76) and the Stonard *Ding dong bell* (No. 75), despite their greater complexity and wider range, and I hope that singers will enjoy meeting the challenge.

The rough classification of the items according to the themes of the words may help the singers to 'sense the music behind the notes'. Those who concentrate exclusively on the music are apt to sound unmusical; those who catch the spirit of the words are well on the way to a fit performance of the music, too.

A word about the title. All rounds are canons, but not all canons are rounds. Rounds are distinguished by the presence of all these characteristics: (1) they are for voices; (2) the leading part completes a whole musical phrase, or even a sentence, before the second voice enters; (3) the second and subsequent parts follow their predecessors at equal intervals of time; (4) all parts enter at the same pitch; (5) each voice, on completing the tune, can start again, so that theoretically the canon could be endless. As an example, No. 77 (*Non nobis Domine*), is not a round, because 2, 3 and 4 are absent.

KENNETH SIMPSON

I MUSIC

1 Con brio Praetorius

Vi - va, vi - va la Mu - si - ca, Vi - va, vi - va la Mu - si - ca,

Vi - va la Mu - si - ca.

Pronounce: Veevah lah Moozeekah
Long live Music.

2 Maestoso Praetorius

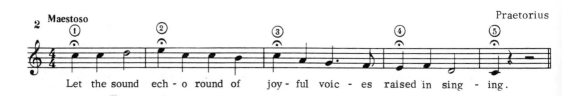

Let the sound ech - o round of joy - ful voic - es raised in sing - ing.

Words taken from *Music through the Recorder,* Book 2, page 11, by Kenneth Simpson, and published by Thomas Nelson & Sons, Limited.

3 Moderato Sartorius

Mu - sic makes glad the hearts of all man - kind; It

makes both young and old leave their cares be - hind.

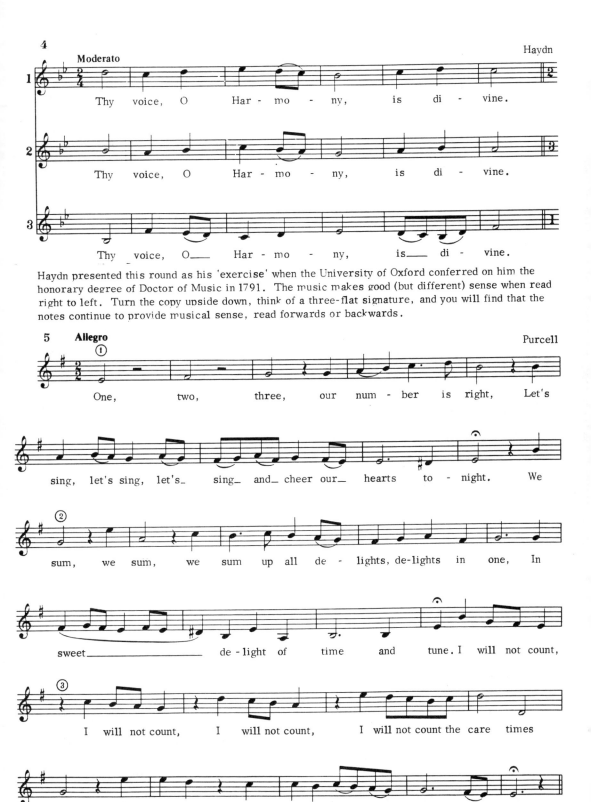

4   Haydn

Moderato

1. Thy voice, O Har - mo - ny, is di - vine.

2. Thy voice, O Har - mo - ny, is di - vine.

3. Thy voice, O__ Har - mo - ny, is__ di - vine.

Haydn presented this round as his 'exercise' when the University of Oxford conferred on him the honorary degree of Doctor of Music in 1791. The music makes good (but different) sense when read right to left. Turn the copy upside down, think of a three-flat signature, and you will find that the notes continue to provide musical sense, read forwards or backwards.

5   **Allegro**   Purcell

① One, two, three, our num - ber is right, Let's

sing, let's sing, let's_ sing_ and_ cheer our_ hearts to - night. We

② sum, we sum, we sum up all de - lights, de-lights in one, In

sweet_____ de - light of time and tune. I will not count,

③ I will not count, I will not count, I will not count the care times

bring, I'll on - ly, I'll on - ly count my_ time to_ sing.

II LEARNING MUSIC

6 **Allegro** moderato

Beethoven

As a fa-vour, please sing for me the scale of C. La la la la la la la la, La la la la la la la la, La la la la la la la la, La la la la la la la la.

Solfeggio 1

7 **Con moto**

Doh' te lah soh fah me ray doh doh ray me fah soh lah te soh doh' te lah te doh' te lah soh fe soh lah soh lah te doh' soh me doh fah me ray soh fah me ray doh.

Solfeggio 2

8 **Moderato**

Doh te, lah, te, lah, soh, lah, soh, fah, lah, soh, fah, me, me, fah, soh, lah, te, doh ray me fah me ray me ray doh ray doh te, te, doh doh_____ te, lah,

9 **Moderate speed, not too smugly**

Haydn

Sing high doh' and te, doh' lah, doh' soh, doh' fah, doh' me, doh' ray, doh' doh.____ ____ To sing the notes of__ a - ny__ air We prac-tise with the great-est care; and so it comes that__ ve - ry soon We sing them ev-'ry one in tune.

Solfeggio 3

10 **Moderato**

Doh ray, doh me, doh fah fah, doh soh, doh lah, doh te, doh doh' soh me doh, doh' te, doh' taw,* doh' lah, doh' soh, doh' fah soh fah me ray, ray doh me soh doh'.

* usually spelt *ta*

The pupil's complaint

19th century?

11 **Allegro**

Doh ray me fah, I'm quite tired of this sol-fa-ing, I for-get all you've been say-ing.

The teacher's reply

Kenneth Simpson

12 **Allegro**

Soh fah me ray, This sol-fa-ing's just the thing to help us with the songs we sing.--

The teacher's reply can be sung simultaneously with the previous round, making eight parts in all.

13 **Andante**

19th century?

Sound for us, O e - cho sweet, e - cho sweet, Soft - ly now our song re- peat. Gen-tle e - cho, wake from sleep, Gen-tle e - cho clear and deep.

The mumbler's round

19th century?

14 **Moderato, con severità**

Wheth-er you whis - per low, or loud - ly call, Speak clear - ly, speak clear - ly or don't speak, don't speak at all.

III TIMES AND SEASONS

15 **Allegro**

Hans Lang

Wake up!___ The day's be-gun, the night's a-way, the day's be-gun. Wake up!___

Taken from *Der Singkreisel* by permission of Schott & Co. Ltd.

16 **Andante**

Sartorius

Now good-night, I must a-way; we'll meet a-gain an-oth-er day.

Voices finish singly, or first voice sustains its final D until the second voice finishes.

17 **Andante**

Albert Thate

A - bide with us, O Lord, for eve-ning shades are

fall - ing, and the day has reached its end - ing.

Taken from *Bruder Singer* by permission of Bärenreiter Verlag, Kassel.

18 **Andante**

Beethoven

A - cross the lake the sun's last rays Soft-ly fade,

soft-ly__ fade. A-gainst the wa-ter's som-bre_ blue The pines are

etched in sa-bler hue, are_ etched in sa - bler hue. A-bove the

hill the eve-ning__ star gleams a - far,__ gleams a - far.

22 **Allegro** non troppo

English, 13th century

Sum- mer is a - com - ing in,___ Loud - ly sing, cuc - koo.

Grow - eth seed and blow - eth mead, And springs the wood a - new.

Sing, cuc - koo! Ew - e bleat - eth af - ter lamb, Loweth

af - ter cal - ve cow. Bul - lock stert - eth, buck - e vert - eth,

Mer - ry sing, cuc - koo! Cuc - koo, cuc - koo,___

Well sing'st thou, cuc - koo,___ Nor cease thou nev - er now.

Two-part ostinato

Sing, cuc - koo now,___ Sing, cuc - koo!

Sing, cuc - koo! Sing, cuc - koo now,___

23 **Allegro**

K.S.

Har - vest home!___ The boughs do shake and the

bells__ do ring, So mer - ri - ly comes our har - vest in.

Words taken from *The Oxford Books of Verse for Juniors*, edited by James Britton (Book 2, 1957).

24 **Molto moderato**

K.S.

Win - ter has come, the wind's a-whist-ling cold, Skies dark - en,

clouds are heav - y - la - den and the sheep clus - ter close in the fold.

IV CHRISTMAS

25 Allegro

Traditional

Christ-mas is com - ing and then the New Year,

Cold is the night___ and the stars shine out clear, Cold the

night, and the stars shine out clear.

26

Handel (adapted)

Allegro

And the glo - ry the glo-ry of the Lord__ shall

be re - veal - ed.

27 Moderato

Melchior Vulpius

See, where a rose___ is new- ly un - furled, The choic- est

bloom_____ the world has yet known, Which an-cient proph - ets said__

__would come_ to be, And from the stem of Jes - se has grown.

10

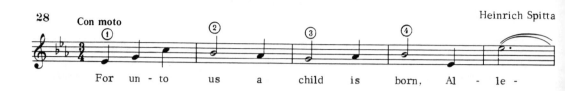

For un - to us a child is born, Al - le -
- lu - ia, Al - le, - al - le - lu - ia.

By permission of Möseler Verlag, Wolfenbüttel.

Glo - ry be— to God on high, Glo -

And— on earth peace, peace,

Good will— to-wards men, good-will— to-wards men, good -

except last time *last time*

- - ry be to God on high, God— on high.

peace,___ and on earth peace, earth— peace.

will, good-will to-wards men, Good - will___ to-wards men. — to-wards men.

V GREETINGS

* If the Coda is not used, finish on the bracketed pauses.

32 Allegro moderato

CODA

K.S.

Birth-day greet-ings, Ma-ny hap-py re - turns of the day, re - turns of the day!

All good wish- es, Ma-ny hap-py re - turns of the day,— re - turns of the day.

Best of luck! Ma-ny hap-py re-turns of the day,— re - turns of the day.

To a bride

33 Andante, teneramente

Hayes

Bloom of beau - ty, ear - ly flow'r, Bloom of beau -

pride— and care, Thou thy

pledge of mu-tual love, Love-ly

- ty, ear - ly flow'r, Of the bliss - ful

pa - rents' pride— and care, Fair - est off - spring

pledge— of mu - tual love, An - gel seem - ing

except last time

bri - dal bow'r, Thou thy pa - rents' bow'r.

of— the fair, Love - ly fair.

last time

from a - bove. Bloom of beau - ty, -bove.

VI GUSTO

34 Vigoroso — Beethoven

Life is for liv-ing, for liv - - - ing, for liv-ing, for liv - ing with joy and good fel-low-ship.

35 Allegro

Let's drink and sing till the raf-ters ring.

36 Con moto

Now Ro-bin lend to me thy bow, Sweet Ro-bin lend to me thy bow, That I may now a-hunt - ing with my la-dy go, with my sweet la - dy go.

37 Allegro — Formerly attributed to Byrd

Hey ho! to the green-wood now let us go, Sing heave and ho!
Hey ho! to the green - wood now let us go, Sing heave and
Hey ho! to the

And there shall we find both buck and doe, Sing heave and go, Sing heave and ho! And there shall we find both buck and green - wood now let us go, Sing heave and ho! And there shall we

14

ho! The hart and hind. and the lit-tle pret - ty roe,Sing heave_ and

doe, Sing heave and ho! The hart and hind and the lit-tle pret - ty

find both buck and doe, Sing heave_ and The hart and

ho! Hey ho! to the green-wood now let us

roe, Sing heave_ and ho! Hey ho! to the

hind and the lit-tle pret - ty roe, Sing heave and ho! Hey

38 Urgentemente

Some - thing in- side me says, 'Time for my tea! Time for my tea! Time for my tea!'

39 Moderato

Tab- le's set and food is rea - dy; Let's be - gin! Let's be - gin!

Taken from *Der Ring bind't alle Ding* by permisson of Barenreiter Verlag, Kassel.

40 Allegro Samuel Webbe

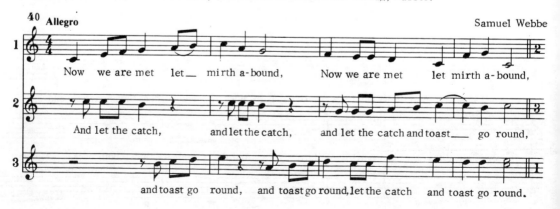

Now we are met let_ mirth a-bound, Now we are met let mirth a-bound,

And let the catch, and let the catch, and let the catch and toast_ go round,

and toast go round, and toast go round, let the catch and toast go round.

VII DROLLERY

41 Con sdegno

Chr. Lahusen

Some say Welsh-men nev - er sing! Hosts of full - voiced

Cam - brian choirs Will show them up for li - ars!_____

Taken from *Nederlands Volkslied* by Pollmann & Tiggers by permission of Uitgverij De Tooets, Haarlem.

The accident

42 Poco allegro

K.S.

Send for the doc - tor! Nel - lie's fal - len down and crocked her

El - bow and fun - ny bone: A bus came a - long and knocked her.

They'll come and fetch her, put her on a stretch - er, Get her all right o - ver-night.

Recorder — *Introduction*

Cymbal Drum and Tambourine

The introduction can also be played with the last bar of the singing to finish the performance.

43 Moderato

Some-thing's wrong, and the farm-er's out of luck: All his hens be-gin to crow, and the

cock-'rels go cluck! cluck! Cock - a- doo-dle doo! Cluck- e-ty, cluck, cluck, cluck!

Taken from *Kinderzang en Kinderspel*, part 2, by Kes, Pollmann & Tiggers by permission of Uitgeverij De Toorts, Haarlem.

Taken from *Nederlands Volkslied* by Pollmann & Tiggers by permission of Uitgeverij De Toorts, Haarlem.

The metronome round

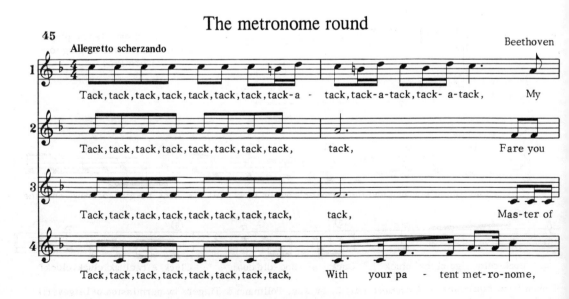

dear__ friend Jo - hann Mäl - zel.

well, good - bye.

time, mas - ter of time, tack - a - tack, tack - a -

pa - tent met - ro - nome, tack - a - tack, tack - a -

46 Allegretto scherzando   Lachner

1 If I know what you know, and you know what I know, then

2 I know then what you know, I know then what

3 If I know what you know, and you know what I know,

I know what you know, and you know what I know.

you know, and you know, and you know what I know.

I know then what you know, And you know what I know.

47 Allegro

① Why should-n't my goose Be as fat as your goose,

③ When I paid for my goose ④ Twice as much as you?

18

VIII GETTING AROUND

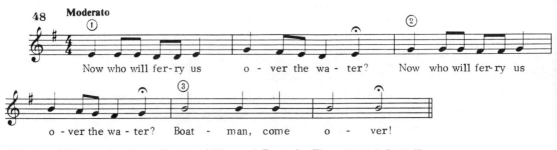

48 Moderato

Now who will fer-ry us o - ver the wa - ter? Now who will fer-ry us o - ver the wa - ter? Boat - man, come o - ver!

Words and Music taken from *Shepherds' Pipes and Tunes for Them*, E.M.G.Liddell
© 1932 Yearbook Press, Ascherberg, Hopwood & Crew Ltd.

49 Con moto   M.E. McGee

My padd-le's keen and bright, Flash-ing—with sil - ver. Fol-low—the wild goose flight,

Dip, dip, and swing.

Barcarolle

19th century?

Glide_____ a - long,_____ my bon - ny boat,

While with the tide we gent - ly float, and chant to the deep— sea's mel - low note;

Glide_____ a - long,_____ my bon - ny, bon - ny boat.

Accompaniment

51 Allegro non troppo

Horse to trot, to trot, I say;

am - ble and am - ble and make a stay, and

gal - lop and gal - lop and gal-lop a - way.

IX BIRDS AND BEASTS

Con moto

52

As I me walk - ed in a May___ morn-ing I heard a bird sing Cuc - koo!

Allegretto   William Stonard

53

Cuc - koo! Good neigh-bours help us to hedge in the cuc - koo, Keep, keep, keep, oh keep in the cuc - koo!

54 **Moderato**   19th century?

1 Sweet the pleas-ure of___ the spring When we hear the cuc - koo sing;

2 Cuc-koo, cuc-koo, cuc-koo, cuc-koo, When we hear the cuc - koo sing.

3 There! Where? There! cuc-koo, cuc-koo, cuc-koo, Hear the cuc-koo sing.

Cheerfully

55

Here we come to sing our song! Chick-ens' ears are ve - ry short and don - keys' long.

Allegro

56

Where is John?___ The old red hen has left her pen. Where is John?___ The cows are in the corn a-gain, O John!_____

57 **Allegro**

My dame hath a lame, tame crane, My dame hath a crane that is lame.

Pray gen-tle Jane, let my dame's lame tame_ crane_ Feed and come home a - gain.

X MISCELLANEA

58 Tempo di ballo ① ② Traditional

I'll take my fid-dle if you'll bring your flute, Then I'll scrape the cat-gut while

you blow, Toot, Toot. I'll scrape the gut, you blow, Toot, Toot.

59 Allegretto ① ② French

Oh, the pret-ty lit-tle mill; It goes tick-a, tick-a, tick-a, tick, tack, tick, tack,

night and day. It goes tick-a, tick-a, tick-a, tick-a, tick, tack, night and day.

60 Maestoso ① ② ③

Poor men, take cour-age: Those who have noth-ing, noth-ing have to lose.

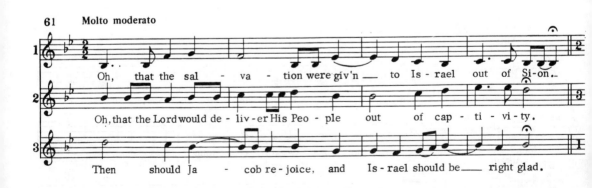

61 Molto moderato

1. Oh, that the sal - va - tion were giv'n — to Is - rael out of Si - on.

2. Oh, that the Lord would de - liv-er His Peo - ple out of cap - ti - vi - ty.

3. Then should Ja - cob re - joice, and Is - rael should be — right glad.

From the one-act comic opera *The Perfect Fool*. Sung by three pitcher-carriers as they approach the well. (Transposed)

Copyright Novello & Company Limited 1923

22

66 Moderato

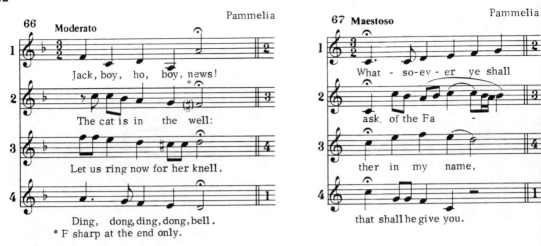

1. Jack, boy, ho, boy, news!
2. The cat is in the well:
3. Let us ring now for her knell.
4. Ding, dong, ding, dong, bell.

* F sharp at the end only.

67 Maestoso

1. What - so-ev - er ye shall
2. ask of the Fa -
3. ther in my name,
4. that shall he give you.

68 Allegro

Bu - gles call- ing, call - ing, call- ing, Bu - gles call - ing, call - ing, call-ing, make the ech - oes ring!

69 Moderato

Wind from the north or wind from the east Brings no luck to man or beast; South or west is best.

70 Con moto

Heave ho, heave and ho, Heave a-way my John-nies, heave and ho, Heave ho, heave and ho, Heave a-way my John-nies, heave and ho, Heave a-way my John-nies, heave and ho, Heave and ho, and

71 Moderato

All in - to ser - vice, Let us sing mer- ri - ly to -
geth - er: Ding, dong, ding, dong, bell.

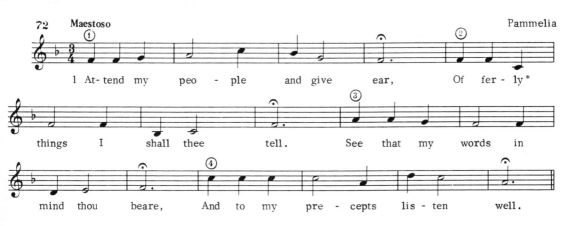

72 Maestoso · Pammelia

1 At- tend my peo - ple and give ear, Of fer - ly*
things I shall thee tell. See that my words in
mind thou beare, And to my pre - cepts lis - ten well.

2 I am thy sovereigne Lord and God,
Which have thee brought from carefull thrall;
And eke †reclaimed from Pharaoh's rod,
Make thee no gods on them to call.

3 Nor fashioned form of any thing,
In heaven or earth to worship it:
For I thy God by revenging
With grievous plagues this sinne will smite.

* ferly = wonderfully great
† eke = also

Optional prelude

Maestoso · K.S.

f

73 Allegretto · K.S.

Glo - ry to God in the high - est, Peace on earth,_ good -
will_ towards men, Good - will, good - will to all men.

24

74 **Moderato**　①　②　③　④ *　Israeli

Give peace on_earth, give peace on_earth, give peace on___ earth, Good -

will to-wards men, good - will to-wards men, Give peace, Lord___ on_ earth.

* Extra voices can continue to enter at one-bar intervals.

75 **Lento**　①　William Stonard

Ding, ding, ding, dong bell. Ding, ding, ding, ding, dong bell. Hark!

hark! they ring: 'tis for the bur - y - ing of poor John Fell. A -

lack and well a-way! 'tis a hea - vy day that ev - er_ us be - fell. Then

for his sake some or-der let us take, that we may ring his knell.

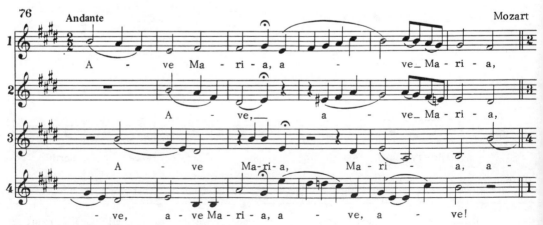

76 **Andante**　Mozart

1　A - ve Ma - ri - a, a - ve_ Ma - ri - a,

2　A - ve,___ a - ve_ Ma - ri - a,

3　A - ve Ma - ri - a, Ma - ri - a, a -

4　- ve, a - ve Ma - ri - a, a - ve, a - ve!

Pronounce: Ahvay Mareea.
　Hail, Mary.

77 Moderato

Formerly attributed to Byrd

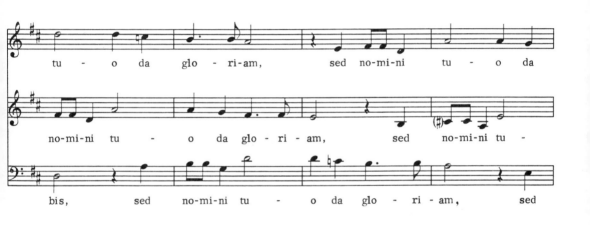

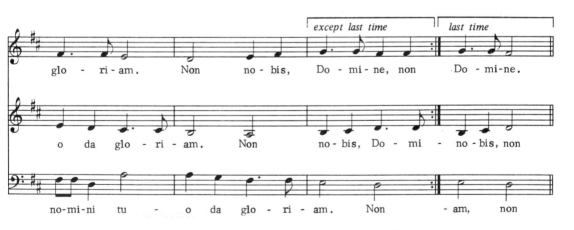

Pronounce : Non nohbeece Domeenay, sayd nomeenee too-oh dah glawreeahm.
Not unto us, O Lord, but to Thy name be glory given.

2/09(168797)
Printed in England